Galway in Stone –
A geological walk in the
heart of Galway

Compiled by Martin Feely

With contributions from Jon Hunt, Jerry Lidwill
and Kevin Barton.
Graphics : Jon Hunt and Martin Feely

A reduced size image of the share certificates issued by the Galway
Granite Quarry and Marble Works Ltd. (see page 19).

This publication has received support from the Heritage
Council under the 2002 Publications Grant Scheme.

Published by Geoscapes, 3 Fontenoy Street, Dublin 7, Ireland
© Geoscapes
ISBN 0-9543412-0-1
2002

All photographs by Paraig O'Connor
© westerneyes-photography
www.westerneyes-photography.com

Printed by Leinster Leader Ltd., Naas, Co.Kildare

Contents

Foreword

This book deals mainly with the geology and use of shaped natural stone in the buildings of Galway. The geological elements of the book include an introduction to the classification of rocks and a simple description of Galway's bedrock geology. These are set in a concise historical framework through which the history of building and quarrying in the Galway region is highlighted. The core of the book involves a geological walk, with accompanying map, around Galway's inner city to view the fascinating range of local and imported building stones that display textures, structures and fossils which give us clues as to their origin and in turn tell us much about Earth history. In addition, we can see the effects of weathering on the city's building stones and view examples of geological processes in action today such as rock weathering and water dissolution products growing on our limestone buildings. The tour can be followed by our city's visitors and geologists alike and will prove very useful for urban fieldwork by primary, secondary and third level student parties. Furthermore, it provides an opportunity to study rocks from around the globe e.g. China, Finland, Portugal, Italy, South Africa, Norway, Brazil, England and of course Ireland in a matter of two to three hours. The book is an invitation to enjoy learning about the geological heritage that surrounds us in the heart of Galway.

Dr. Martin Feely,
Geology Department.,
NUI, Galway.
2002.

Figure 1.1 Opposite. The rock cycle or "new rocks for old". The cycle involves the generation of new igneous rocks from the Earths mantle and by melting older sedimentary and metamorphic rocks - existing rocks fall victim to the agents of erosion on the Earth's surface(e.g. wind, water and ice) which in turn provide the fodder for sedimentary rocks and so the cycle has continued throughout the Earth's 4.5 billion year history.

Chapter 1.
The Bedrock Geology of Galway

Introduction

Rocks are divided on the basis of their origin into three major groups: igneous, metamorphic and sedimentary rocks. The rock cycle (figure 1.1) shows the formation of igneous rocks from magma (molten rock material); the effects of surface weathering and erosion to produce sedimentary rocks; and the effects of pressure and heat deep in the Earth's crust to produce metamorphic rocks. The minerals that make up igneous rocks crystallise from a _magma_, the minerals of metamorphic rocks form in response to elevated pressure and/or temperature acting on pre-existent rocks, while most sedimentary rocks are composed of minerals inherited from older eroded rocks. Each of the major rock groups is further subdivided according to well established criteria based upon mineral compositions and rock textures (Press and Siever 1998). **Throughout the book words that are underlined and in italics are explained in the glossary.**

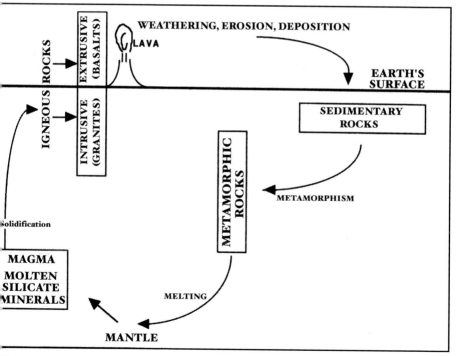

Figure 1.1 The rock cycle

Igneous rocks

Igneous rocks consist of interlocking crystals formed from the cooling and con-solidation of molten _magma_. Intrusive or plutonic rocks occur when the magma solidifies beneath the earth's crust. These rocks cool very slowly resulting in coarse-grained crystalline rocks like _granite_ or _gabbro_. Extrusive or volcanic rocks are formed when molten lava pours out onto the Earth's surface through surface cracks and fissures or via volcanoes. In this setting a much more rapid rate of magma cooling leads to significantly finer grained rocks like _basalt_ and _rhyolite_. In the building stone trade most igneous rocks are called granites since they are hard, crystalline and take a good polish. The granites are represent-ed in Galway by our own local granite i.e. Galway Granite, and by granites from Leinster, Finland, Portugal and China. "Black Granite" which is not granite but a variety of _gabbro_ is also used in the city buildings and all of it probably sourced in South Africa (figure 1.2).

Sedimentary rocks

Sedimentary rocks form from the accumulation and compaction of sediment. They consist almost entirely (>95%) of _sandstones_, _mudstones_ and carbonates The latter are composed largely of the mineral calcite (calcium carbonate $CaCO_3$) and /or dolomite (calcium magnesium carbonate $CaMgCO_3$) and are referred to as limestones. Limestones can form due to chemical precipitation e.g. travertine or they may be composed of fossils and formed by accumulation in shallow subtropical seas. This is how the Galway limestones formed some 350 million years ago. In the case of travertine it was formed from limy carbon-ated water originating from hot springs. It contains cavities formed by carbon dioxide gas bubbles as the limy content of the waters was precipitated out as travertine. Limestone and Italian travertine are used in the city (figure 1.2).

Metamorphic rocks

When pre-existing rocks are subjected to elevated temperatures and /or pres-sures they undergo textural and mineralogical changes. This process of change called metamorphism occurs deep in the earth's crust when rocks become buried due to the relative movements of the Earth's _tectonic plates_. If the pre-existing rock is monomineralic only textural changes will occur. Thus quartz sandstones become _quartzites_ and calcite limestones change to white calcite _marble_. In contrast polymineralic rocks undergo textural and mineralogica changes e.g. mudstones form _slates_ and _schists_, granites can be converted to granite _gneiss_ and basalt and gabbro change to _amphibolite_. Marbles from Italy Portugal and Connemara are used in the city's buildings (figure 1.2)

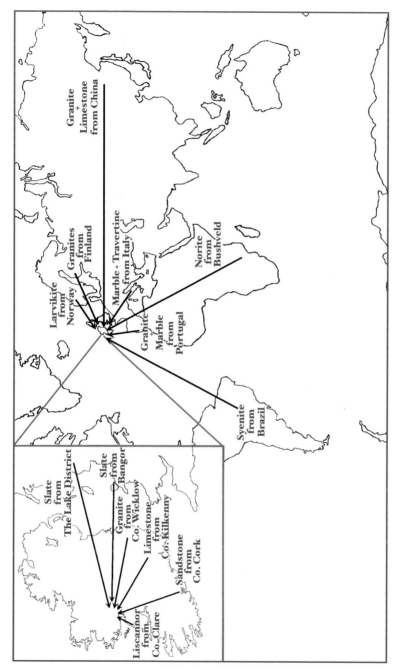

Granite + Limestone from China

Granites from Finland

Larvikite from Norway

Marble + Travertine from Italy

Norite from Bushveld

Granite + Marble from Portugal

Syenite from Brazil

Slate from The Lake District

Slate from Bangor

Granite from Co. Wicklow

Limestone from Co. Kilkenny

Sandstone from Co. Cork

Liscannor from Co. Clare

Figure 1.2 Global map showing the provenance of Galway's building stones.

7

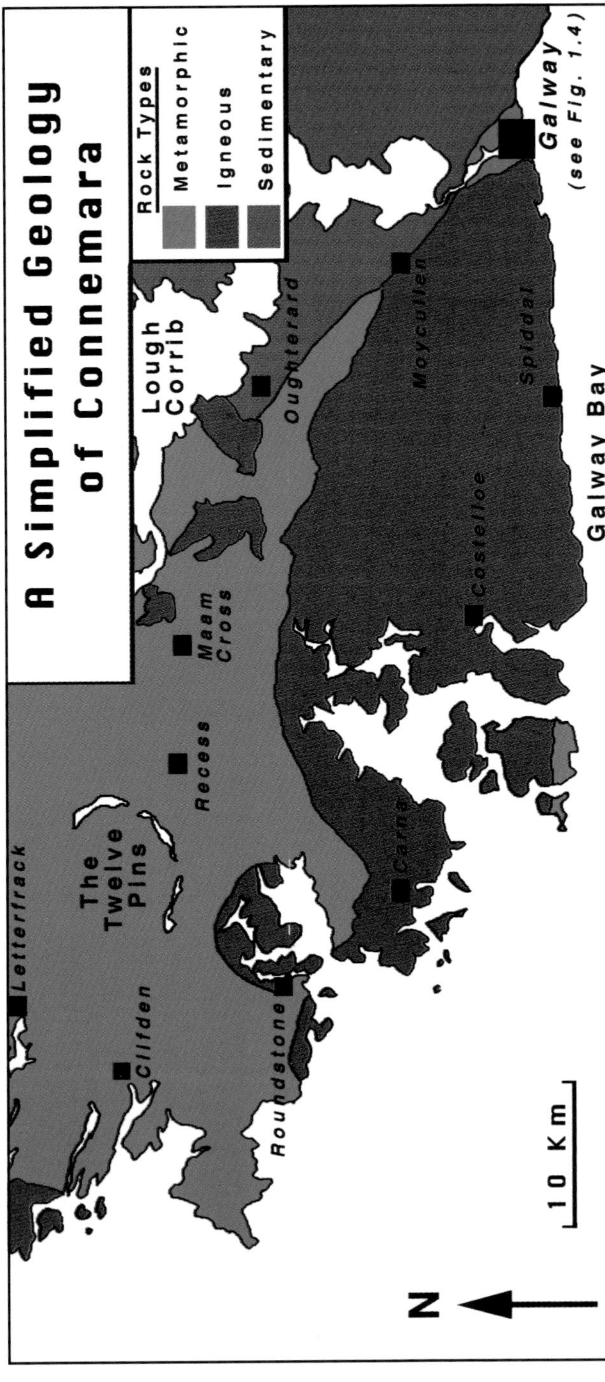

Figure 1.3
A simplified regional
geological map of
South Connemara.

A Simplified Geology of Connemara

Rock Types

Metamorphic
Igneous
Sedimentary

Lough Corrib

Galway (see Fig. 1.4)

Oughterard

Moycullen

Spiddal

Castelloe

Galway Bay

Maam Cross

Recess

The Twelve Pins

Carna

Letterfrack

Clifden

Roundstone

10 Km

N

8

Bedrock geology of Galway

Galway is built on a geological mosaic of metamorphic, igneous and sedimentary rocks covered by a relatively thin skin of recent (<1 million years old) glacial sand and gravel deposits (Coats and Wilson 1971). The distribution of these rock types reflects a fundamental geological divide between the eastern and western regions of Co.Galway. The metamorphic and igneous rocks make up the bedrock of the South Connemara region to the west (Leake and Tanner 1994). The sedimentary rocks, mostly *Carboniferous* limestones, extend eastwards forming the bedrock of the Irish Midlands (figures 1.3 and 1.4).

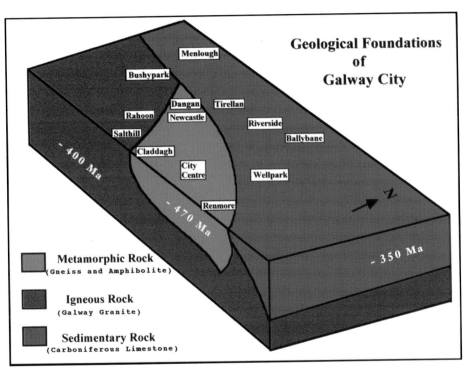

Figure 1.4 A block diagram showing the bedrock geology of Galway and its surrounds. The oldest part of the city is coincidentally built on the oldest rocks.

The metamorphic rocks of Galway

Galway's inner city which is the oldest part of the city was coincidentally founded on the oldest rocks which are amphibolite and granite gneiss (figures 1.3 and 1.4). These were originally igneous rocks (gabbro and granite) formed about 470 ± 5 million years ago (mya). However, during this time metamorphic processes exerted their influence on these igneous rocks and converted them to amphibolite and granite gneiss. Other manifestations of this metamorphism are the corrugated quartzite mountains of the Twelve Pins and their intricate multicoloured layers of the renowned Connemara Marble. The amphibolite and granite gneiss can be observed in many of the dry stone walls in the inner part of the city e.g. along the canal and opposite the Cathedral. The amphibolite is easily recognised by its dark grey colour which reflects a dominance of a dark iron bearing mineral called _hornblende_. The Gate Lodge at the main entrance to NUI, Galway is mainly built from this stone. The Corrib River cuts through this dark grey rock and forms its steep banks at the Salmon Weir Bridge for example. The Galway Docks are located on this rock type also - Wilkinson (1845) in alluding to the amphibolite bedrock states that it

"was met with in the sinkings for the new docks, and from the difficulty of quarrying it, caused great loss to the contractor."

Needless to say this stone found little favour with the builders of the city. The granite gneiss, lighter grey in colour, is essentially a banded granite. It is spatially related to the amphibolite and both can be seen together in the some of the blocks in the inner city walls.

The Connemara Marble has been quarried for centuries and records go back to at least the 18th century (see Chapter 2). Ideal as an ornamental and decorative stone, and very popular in the manufacture of jewellery, it is unsuited to exterior building purposes, as it loses its colour when exposed to the elements over a long period, but has been widely used for panelling, pillars, fireplaces and other interior work. The interior of Galway Cathedral offers a spectacular example of the use of Connemara Marble as interior floor tiles.

The igneous rocks of Galway

The bedrock geology along the Northern shoreline of Galway Bay is dominated by granite (figure 1.3). Many varieties are encountered in the region and they range in colour from pink to dark grey reflecting varying proportions of the three minerals e.g. _feldspar_, _quartz_ and _mica_. All varieties are collectively termed the Galway Granite which formed from a magma about 400 million years ago. Proceeding westwards from the city centre to Salthill the bedrock geology changes from amphibolite and gneiss to the granite (figures 1.3 and 1.4). Outcrops of the Granite can be observed along the beaches at Salthill and westwards along the coast to west of Roundstone. The 19th century Claddagh Dominican Church was built from Galway granite.

The sedimentary rocks of Galway

Proceeding eastwards from the city centre the amphibolite and granite gneiss gives way to the Carboniferous limestone which is the youngest of the three bedrock varieties. The term "Carboniferous" comes from England, in reference to the rich deposits of coal that formed during this period. The Limestone (figure 1.5) of the Galway region formed during the early stages of this period (~350 mya). Shallow subtropical seas, in which marine life (e.g. corals and shellfish varieties) abounded, was the environment for the formation of the limestone—a setting akin to todays Great Barrier Reef off the west coast of Australia.

This limestone has provided the Galway region with a huge natural resource of building stone. Local quarries at Angliham, Menlough and Merlin Park provided cut limestone blocks that have been used extensively over the centuries in the building of Galway city. The local and imported building stones used in Galway are set in a lithological and geological time framework in figure 1.6.

Figure 1.5 Horizontally bedded limestone in the modern aggregate quarry at Menlough.

11

Era	Geological Period		Igneous and Metamorphic	Sedimentary
Cenozoic	Quaternary	1		Sands and Gravels (Galway) Travertine (Italy) [28]
Cenozoic	Tertiary	65		
Mesozoic	Cretaceous	144		
Mesozoic	Jurassic	200	Carrara Marble [4]	
Mesozoic	Triassic	250		
Palaeozoic	Permian	300	Larvikite [33] Portuguese Granite [1]	
Palaeozoic	Carboniferous	355		Limestone (Galway) [26] Limestone (Kilkenny) [15]
Palaeozoic	Devonian	418	Galway Granite [14] Scandinavian Granites [48]	Cork Red Sandstone [4]
Palaeozoic	Silurian	440	Burlington Slate [35]	
Palaeozoic	Ordovician	490	Amphibolite/Gneiss (Galway) [2] Connemara Marble [4]*	
Palaeozoic	Cambrian	544		
Archean	Precambrian		Granite (Rapakivi, Finland) [36] Gabbro/Norite (Bushveld) [35] Oldest Known Rocks on Earth are ~ 4200 million years old (Acasta Gneisses, Canada)	
Archean	Formation of the Earth ~ 4600			

Figure 1.6 A lithological and geological time framework for the local and imported building stones of Galway. The numbers in brackets refer to the locations of these buildings stones in the tour guide map inside the back cover.

* Connemara Marble is a metamorphosed impure limestone which was originally formed during the Precambrian Period.

Chapter 2
A History of Dimension Stone Quarrying in Galway

Introduction

Shaped natural stone is usually called dimension stone, and the industry involved in quarrying, shaping, dressing and polishing this stone is called the dimension stone industry and plays a key role within the larger building construction industry (Smith 1999). A good dimension stone is one that is devoid of cracks, robust and is free of minerals that weather easily and/or breakdown chemically. The durability and weathering resistance of natural dimension stone means that it can be exposed to the elements without needing any surface coating such as rendering. It is also very versatile and can be used to construct a wide range of architectural or structural forms and has been used throughout the ages for walls, arches, pillars, domes and of course pyramids. Dimension stone is used in a variety of ways from load-bearing blocks to non load-bearing exterior and interior cladding panels. It is also used for flooring and roofing. When used in the immediate surrounds of buildings e.g. walkways and road paving it comes under the heading of hard landscaping.

Dimension stone constantly competes in the market place with man-made cements, brick and ceramic tiles. It enjoys however, a good reputation as a non load-bearing natural material, and is used extensively today for exterior and interior cladding and for ornamental and monumental works.

In Galway, the local availability of suitable dimension stone resources in the form of limestone and granite led to the growth of a city which is dominated by great natural stone buildings built from the 14th century to the 20th century (see Garner 1985). These include churches, civic buildings, financial houses and private dwelling houses; most of these were built of locally quarried limestone. The use of natural stone in Galway, has developed from the traditional utilisation of local stone to the importation of stone from all over the world mainly for use as non load bearing exterior (and interior) panelling and for hard landscaping. Galway for example, uses granites from Scandinavia, Portugal and China, Portuguese and Italian marbles, South African and Brazilian stone in addition to Irish stone from Leinster, Kilkenny, Cork and Liscannor (see figure 1.2). In addition, exterior and interior panels of the world famous Connemara marble obviously form an important part of the city's building heritage.

In earlier centuries, the choice of material used in building was dictated primarily by local geology. Transportation was difficult and expensive, and consequently quarries were small and used solely for local building purposes. A quarry might be opened for the construction of an individual castle or church, then never worked again. These small, scattered quarries are dispersed throughout Co. Galway. The development of canals and railways in the 18th century brought an improvement in communications which radically altered traditional practices in the quarrying of stone. These developments were slow to reach the West of Ireland, but the construction of the Galway -Clifden - Westport road by Alexander Nimmo in the 1850's and the opening of the Galway - Clifden railway in 1895, opened a new chapter in the history of quarrying in Connemara. The smaller quarries began to close down, while the larger ones expanded their output.

The Connemara Marble Quarries

Of all the rock types to be found in Ireland, the Connemara marble is the most celebrated. It occurs as discontinuous exposures for about 30 km in an east-west direction along the southern flanks of the Twelve Pins (na Beanna Beola). It is ideal as an ornamental and decorative stone, and very popular in the manufacture of jewellery, it is unsuited to exterior building purposes, as it loses its colour when exposed to the elements over a long period, but has been widely

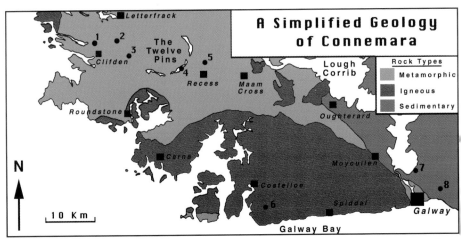

Figure 2.1 Simplified geological map of South Connemara showing the locations of the Connemara marble (1. Streamstown, 2. Creggs, 3. Barnanoraun, 4. Derryclare, 5. Lissoughter.) , Galway granite (6. Costelloe.) and Galway limestone (7. Angliham / Menlough, 8. Merlin.) quarries.

Figure 2.2 Connemara marble quarry at Streamstown. Note the intricate colour patterns produced by the folded marble layers in the quarry. These were produced some 470 million years ago during metamorphism.

used for panelling, pillars, fireplaces and for other interior decorative purposes. It is especially popular in churches, where it is used for furnishings such as pulpits, lecterns and altar rails. There are five principal marble quarries in Connemara, extending from Streamstown in the west to Lissoughter in the east (see figure 2.1 for locations).

The Streamstown quarry is situated about 3 km. northwest of Clifden (figure 2.2). In the 19th century it was worked by the D'Arcy family, who founded the town of Clifden around 1810, and later by a Mr. Colles of Kilkenny. The marble blocks were carted to Clifden for shipment abroad, where they were used for ornamental and decorative work. Streamstown marble was used to pave the chancels of the Cathedrals of Truro (1886), Peterborough (1892) and Bristol (1895), as well as the steps of Worcester Cathedral (1877). In Cambridge it was used in the pillars of the Chapel of St. John's College (1869), and the presbytery of Great St. Mary's Church. The bust of Professor Sedgwick in the Sedgwick Museum, Cambridge was also made of marble from this quarry. There are three principal marble types in this quarry : a white calcite marble, streaked with green and brown and tinged with pink, known as Pinka Grenna; a green *tremolite* marble with white and sepia bands and a green serpentine marble.

The Creggs quarry lies about 2 km south of Letterfrack, on the west side of Lough Nahillion. There are two horizons of green and white marbles, separated by dark grey schists and quartzites. Kinahan (1886) describes the marble from this quarry as being *"eminently suited for delicate cut-stone purposes"* and Sibthorpe of Dublin remarked that it was *"of excellent quality, equal to the Italian, but it rises in small blocks"*. Dr. Ritchie of Belfast encountered a similar problem in attempting to obtain blocks of a marketable size.

The Barnanoraun quarry is situated about 9 km east of Clifden in the Owenmore valley, and consists of a number of separate quarries, in which both green and white marble is to be found. Kinahan(1886) remarks on the presence of pale greenish-grey marble with *dendritic* markings, resembling *moss agate*, and used by Alick McDonnell of Clifden to make ornaments, under the trade name of "moss serpentine". A specimen was presented to the Museum in Queen's College Galway (now NUI, Galway). A fine example of Barnanoraun marble is to be seen in the pillars of the Museum Building in Trinity College Dublin. The main quarry lies to the north of Barnanoraun village. There are also good exposures of green marble along the banks of the Owenglin River to the north. The quarries were first worked in the 1830's by the Martins of Ballynahinch, when they were known as the Ballynahinch Green Marble or Serpentine Quarries. A steep ridge between Owenglin and Ballynahinch, which impeded transportation, did not facilitate operations. The marble blocks had to be carted across the ridge for shipment from Cloonisle pier. Today this quarry is owned and worked by the Joyce family of Recess.

The Derryclare quarry is located on the north east shore of Lough Derryclare, about 3 km north west of Recess. The principal quarry area exposes folded bands of green, yellow-green, white and grey marbles, which are interbedded with amphibolite and schist. An attractive jade green (serpentine -rich) marble, much favoured by jewellery makers, is also to be found in this locality. This quarry was also once worked by the Martin family. This quarry and the Streamstown and Creggs quarries are owned by Connemara Marble Products Ltd., Moycullen, (proprietor: Ambrose Joyce, Galway).

The Lissoughter quarry is situated about 1 km north of Recess. It was worked by the Martins of Ballynahinch, and later by Messrs. Sibthorpe of Dublin. Kinahan(1886) comments that *"very good-sized stones have been raised, but in rough unshapely blocks"*. He also noted that it was known in the trade as Lissoughter Green Marble and sold for 16 shillings per cubic foot. A column nine foot, nine inches high was carved from a block raised in Lissoughter, and adorned St. Anne's in Taylor's Hill - the country mansion of Lord Ardilaun. In England, St. Pancras Station and Hotel and St. John's College Cambridge were among those who made use of this marble, and the chimney-piece presented to King George IV by "Humanity Dick" Martin, and later installed in the Carleton Club, London, was wrought out of serpentine from either the Lissoughter or Barnanoraun quarries. It was also exported to the United States where there was a thriving market for dark green marble, and was used in the composition of the monolithic columns in the entrance hall of the University Club, New York. Lissoughter quarry is operated by J.C. Walsh and Sons Ltd., Dublin.

The role played by the Martins of Ballynahinch in the history of marble quarrying in Connemara is of interest. In 1660, on the Restoration of King Charles to the English throne, "Nimble Dick" Martin (c.1637-1730) acquired a large portion of the lands confiscated from the O' Flahertys by Cromwell. This shrewd lawyer, a Catholic and a Jacobite, not only retained his lands during the reign of the Protestant William of Orange, and the introduction of the Penal Laws against Catholics, but added to them considerably. His great-grandson, "Humanity Dick" Martin (1754-1834), the famous politician, duellist and animal lover, inherited an estate of 192,000 acres in Connemara, including most of the marble resources. It was in his time that marble was discovered in Connemara.

Although the quarries were worked by Dick Martin and his son Thomas, their full commercial potential was never realised, partly due to the lack of roads and railways in the west during that period. But it was the Martins who first had the marble polished, and Thomas Martin had a magnificent pair of oval-topped tables made for Ballynahinch. The profligate lifestyle of the Martins led them into severe financial difficulties, which were compounded by the Famine. In 1850, Mary Martin, "the Princess of Connemara", the last of this branch of the family, emigrated to America, where she died the same year, and the Ballynahinch estate was acquired under the Encumbered Estates Act by Richard Berridge. In the second half of the century, improved communications contributed towards the commercial success of the quarries, which the Martins failed to achieve. The estate was owned in the 1920's by the famous Indian cricketer and statesman Kumar Shri Ranjitsinhji.

The Limestone Quarries

Limestone from the quarries at Angliham and Menlough (see figures 2.1 and 2.3), about 2 km north of Galway was exported extensively to London, Liverpool, Bristol and Glasgow and also enjoyed a flourishing market in America. Wilkinson (1845) noted that the most valuable black marble (in fact a black Galway limestone) quarries in Ireland were situated on the south east shore of Lough Corrib in the townlands of Menlough and Angliham. At Angliham a bed of black limestone was worked and exported to London and America. So great was the demand in London for this variety that the bed was christened the London Bed and the stone was traded as London Black. Kinahan (1869) wrote that the stone was sold for five shillings a foot at Angliham or five shillings and sixpence a foot at the quay in Galway. The stone was transported at that time by barge to the quay. The staircase of the Duke of Hamilton's mansion in Scotland was constructed of black Angliham limestone. As well as the beds of black limestone which was polished and marketed as marble, the quarries also produced a grey limestone, which was used extensively up to recent times as a building stone in Galway. A good example of grey fossiliferous limestone from Angliham can be seen in the Quadrangle building of NUI, Galway, and other examples abound throughout the city. Most of the churches and older institutional and commercial buildings are constructed of limestone from the Lough Corrib quarries. Another quarry, at Terryland, supplied the limestone from which the columns in the Augustinian Church were fashioned.

Figure 2.3   Angliham limestone quarry (Reproduced from Wilkinson, 1845).

The limestone quarry at Merlin Park (figure 2.1), was worked by the Blakes of Merlin Park until c. 1850, and later by Sibthorpes of Dublin. The quarry produced a fossiliferous limestone, which was polished and marketed as a marble known as Merlin Black. There are many examples of this very distinctive stone to be found around the city, especially in the Cathedral (see Chapter 3).

Ballinasloe limestone was quarried at Brackernagh, East Galway. This quarry produced a light to blue-grey limestone and was widely used in Dublin. More recently it has been used extensively in Galway as a cladding stone supplied by Top Quarries, Ballinasloe (Stone Developments Ltd.).

The Granite Quarries

In about 1880, a Scotsman named Millar rented a number of quarries in the Galway area, and set up the Galway Marble and Granite Works, to produce polished marbles and granites for the domestic and foreign markets. The granite quarries worked by Millar included two at Shantalla, which were owned by Colonel Arthur A. Courtnay. The pillars of The Dominican Church in the Claddagh (see Chapter 3), and St. Joseph's Church, Presentation Road, came from this quarry, which also supplied the granite for the base of the Parnell monument in O'Connell Street, Dublin. The Claddagh Dominican Church was also constructed in the late 19th century using a combination of granite and limestone blocks. Granite from these quarries was used in the construction of the Galway Jail, on the site of which the Cathedral now stands. A third quarry at St. Helen's, Taylor's Hill exposed a fine grained red granite, tinged with yellow and speckled with black and white. At Ballagh, near Bushy Park, a granite quarry provided the stone for the pedestal of Dargan's monument on the lawn of Leinster House.

In 1900, Colonel Courtney decided to develop his quarry at Shantalla, and established a company called the Galway Granite Quarry and Marble Works Ltd. (see share certificate on page 2). As well as the granite quarries around Galway city, the Angliham and Menlough limestone quarries were worked by the company for polished "black marble". The company's workshops were situated on the banks of the Eglinton canal, at Earl's Island. At its peak it produced 1,000 tons a week. In 1911 an extension to the Galway-Clifden railway was opened from Distillery Road to the quarry at Shantalla (now part of Maunsell's Park). The last extant evidence of the company was a pillar opposite the Cathedral, on the west side of the entrance to Weir Cottage, which bore a plaque with the name of the company inscribed on it, but, sadly, this has recently disappeared. A quarry of note which is still producing granite is situated at Costelloe in

Connemara (front cover, figure 2.1 and figure 2.4). Here a light pink granite is extracted for building stone. It is known to the geologist as Murvey Granite because it was first recognised and described in the townland of Murvey just west of Roundstone (Wager 1932). This quarry produces cut granite blocks for use as cladding stone in buildings and walls throughout the region.

Figure 2.4 Costelloe "Murvey Granite" quarry - this granite is approx. 380 million years old.

Chapter 3.
A Geological Walk in the Heart of Galway

Introduction

The walking tour highlights the wide variety of local and imported natural stone used in the City's buildings. The guide map inside the back cover displays the locations of the buildings described along the course of the tour. You may wish to complete the full tour which will take three to four hours. However, you can use the map to choose shorter, less time consuming but equally interesting routes. Each building, or where appropriate clusters of buildings, is assigned a location number on the map which is also used in the descriptions below. We have arbitrarily chosen NUI, Galway as the starting point for the tour that takes in fifty locations and ends at the Galway Advertiser's office in Eyre Square.

NUI, GALWAY

The University was founded in 1845, one of the three Queen's Colleges founded in that year in Ireland. Joseph B. Keane designed the **Quadrangle Building (loc.1 -figure 3.1)**, its main tower is a replica of Christopher Wren's Tom Tower in Christ Church College, Oxford. It was constructed in 1848 of cut blocks of

Fig. 3.1
The 19th century Quadrangle building (loc.1) at NUI, Galway built of local Carboniferous limestone. The view from the archway looks across the square to the Aula Maxima. The walkways are paved with Portuguese granite slabs.

fossiliferous _limestone_, from the Angliham quarries at a cost of £38,000. Fossilised remains of _coral_ and _brachiopod_ occur with abundance in the cut blocks. The Quadrangle Building is decorated with _mullioned_ windows and a _crenulated_ _parapet_ flanked by octagonal turrets. On close examination some limestone blocks exhibit thin milky white crusts of carbonate that tend to drape over the blocks. This results from the precipitation of carbonate (calcium carbonate - $CaCO_3$ - called _calcite_) from water containing dissolved calcium carbonate from the limestone. Evaporation and precipitation occurs when the aqueous solution flows over the block. The Quadrangle's tarmacadam footpaths have recently been replaced by _granite_ flagstone pathways. The _flagstones_ were imported from Portugal. This project was undertaken as part of the University's celebrations in 1999 of 150 years since its first Graduation Ceremony. The archway is floored with concrete cobblestones, known in the building trade as Castle Stone.

The **James Mitchell Museum**, is situated in the Quadrangle and contains an impressive collection of rocks, minerals and fossils from all over the world, about 12,000 specimens in all. Noteworthy is the William King (first Professor of Geology) Collection of Permian (290-250 million years ago) fossils, which include many type specimens of great scientific importance. The Eleanor Miles mineral collection, is an eye-catching array of precious and semi-precious stones and other minerals collected from all over the world (Feely and Naughton 1990). Other collections include the mineral and rock collections from the West of Ireland. The Museum was formally designated the James Mitchell Museum in 1977 in recognition of the considerable contributions made by James Mitchell (Prof. of Geology and Mineralogy 1921-1966 and College Secretary and Registrar 1934-1966) to the development of the University -for further information see Harper (1996).

> **The Museum is open to the public and extends a warm welcome to visitors.**

Other additions to the architecture of NUI, Galway include **Arus na Gaeilge, Arts Millennium Building** and the **Martin Ryan Institute**. These buildings are clad with Ballinasloe limestone while **Arus de Brun** is clad with _muscovite schist_ probably from Norway.

At the entrance to the University stands the **Gate-Lodge (loc. 2 -figure 3.2)**, constructed of dressed blocks of limestone and _amphibolite_. The roof is constructed of _slate_ from Bangor in Wales. Portuguese granite slabs identical to those in the Quadrangle, are used in the pathways surrounding the recently renovated lodge.

Fig. 3.2
NUI, Galway's gate -lodge (loc. 2) at the College Road entrance. It is constructed of local dressed blocks of Limestone and dark grey blocks of amphibolite and granite gneiss. The roof slates are either from Killaloe or Bangor.

The **Canal Wall (3)** leading to the boat club, displays examples of the rock types that make up the City's bedrock. Blocks of limestone, granite and amphibolite, combine to create this random rubble wall.

THE CATHEDRAL

The **Cathedral of Our Lady Assumed into Heaven and St. Nicholas (loc. 4 - figure 3.3)** dates from 1965. Dr. Michael Browne, authorised the construction of the present cathedral. The Cathedral was designed by J.J. Robinson of Robinson, Keefe and Devane and was built on the site of the former jail. It ranks as the last great building to be constructed of natural stone in Ireland. It offers

Fig. 3.3
A typical block of fossiliferous Carboniferous limestone used in the construction of The Cathedral of Our Lady Assumed into Heaven and St. Nicholas (inset -loc. 4). The fossils are the entombed remains of shellfish called brachiopods that lived some 350 million years ago in a shallow subtropical sea.

classic examples of the use of natural stone both as load bearing and as ornamental material. Local and imported stone adorn every functional element of the Cathedral's interior space from the Connemara <u>marble</u> floor tiles to the white Italian Carrara marble high altar.

At the entrance to the Cathedral there are gate pillars of Ballinasloe limestone blocks, capped with domes of worked Ballinasloe limestone. These domes contain an abundance of fossil fragments, with fine examples of <u>crinoid</u> remains on show. Outside the building the surrounding area is paved with flagstones, from Liscannor, County Clare, with their distinctive worm or mollusc burrows, known as <u>Olivellites</u>. The Cathedral itself is constructed of cut blocks of limestone sourced from Angliham quarries. These limestone blocks produce a light and dark grey patchwork visible on both the walls and interior arches and pillars (figure 3.4). Connemara marble (from Streamstown quarry) tiles matched with polished and mottled red limestone insets, known as "Cork Red Marble" adorn the floor (figure 3.5).

Fig. 3.4
Interior of the Cathedral look-
ing onto the high altar. The
floor is covered with
Connemara marble, Cork Red
"marble" and Portuguese
marble tiles. Note the dark
and light grey limestone
blocks used in the construc-
tion of the Cathedral walls.

The rails in front of the High Altar are constructed from white Carrara marble while the Altar is constructed of a dark *serpentinite* and marble support on which rests a single slab (5' x 10' x 0.5') of white Carrara marble. The floor surrounding the altar area is of Portuguese beige marble tiles with diamond shaped marble insets (figure 3.6). In the Baptistry, the font is of polished limestone while the walls are panelled with Portuguese marble quarried at Estrimoz, 125 km west of Lisbon (figure 3.7). Note how the marble panels are matched to form kaleidoscope-like patterns using the natural layering in the stone. This cutting and polishing process is known as quartering and is a testament to the skills of the marble workers involved in the construction. The entire Cathedral offers one of the finest examples of the use of natural stone in Ireland -those interested in reading more should read a 32-page publication by the Administrators of

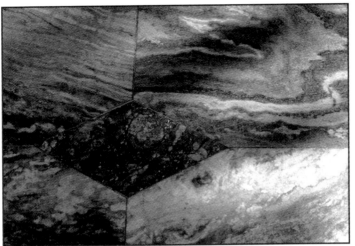

Fig. 3.5
Detail of Conn-
emara marble
floor tiles with
diamond shaped
insets of Cork
Red "marble".
Note the charac-
teristic multilay-
ered nature of the
Connemara mar-
ble showing intri-
cate folded pat-
terns produced
some 470 million
years ago.

Fig. 3.6
Portuguese mar-
ble tiles suround-
ing the high altar.

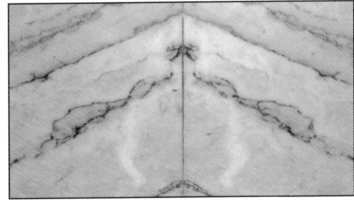

Fig. 3.7
The Baptistry wall
with matched panels
of layered Estrimoz
marble from
Portugal.

Galway Cathedral entitled *Cathedral of Our Lady Assumed into Heaven and St. Nicholas Galway*, published in 1980 by Shanway Publications Ltd., Glengormley, Northern Ireland.

At the rear of the Cathedral is located Nun's Island. **Island House, (loc. 5)** the headquarters of both the County Library and FAS, is constructed of cut limestone blocks. A distinguishing feature of this building is the *dolerite* plaque that bears its name. Further on, the **Arts Centre (loc. 6)** offers another example of the imaginative use of local limestone for building purposes.

DOMINICK STREET

At the corner (No. 65) of Dominick St. and Mill St. stands the **Galway Arms (loc. 7)**. On the wall of this building there can be seen a medieval limestone plaque, depicting the coat of arms of the city. Across the road the **Bridge Mills (loc. 8)** is an old mill constructed of limestone which has been carefully restored, and converted into a restaurant and a mini shopping-centre for arts and crafts. Proceeding down Dominick St., a number of interesting buildings can be seen on the right. **O'Toole's (loc. 9)** newsagents is clad with Connemara marble panels, while **Pasta Paradiso (loc. 10)** the restaurant next door uses Liscannor flagstone. The next two buildings, **No. 47 The Arts Centre and Conradh na Gaeilge (loc. 11)** are both constructed of limestone, and also offer fine examples of Georgian doorways. At the end of the street, the premises of **Kitt, Noone and Co. Chartered Accountants (loc. 12)** are beautifully constructed of limestone and amphibolite blocks, with a some blocks of granite and similar in style and stone work to the19th century Gate-lodge (loc. 2) at the entrance to the University.

Turning left at the end of Dominick St. proceed to the **Fire Station (loc. 13)** where Pink Galway granite blocks capped with limestone are incorporated along it base. Heading towards the Spanish Parade, the statue of **Fr. Tomas de Burca O.P.** stands out as a limestone figure on a limestone-clad base. From here proceed right to the **Dominican Church**, commonly known as the **Claddagh Church (loc.14 -figure 3.8)**. This church was opened on October 25th 1891 and is largely constructed of locally quarried pink Galway granite - indeed it stands as the best example of a granite building in the city. Pillars of locally polished Galway granite adorn the interior and display the characteristic salmon pink *feldspars* that make this a handsome granite (figure 3.9). The Dominican House Chronicle (1921-1962) includes a document describing the Claddagh Church as being 'on the verge of the Atlantic, in glistening Galway granite' (see O'Heideain 1991).

Fig.3.8
The Dominican Church (loc. 14) in the Claddagh built of locally quarried pink Galway granite blocks edged with Galway grey limestone blocks.
Fig. 3.9
Detail of a polished Galway granite support pillar from inside the Dominican Church. Two types of feldspar are visible. The potassium rich salmon pink ortho-clase feldspar (the large crystal on lower right is ~3cm long), and the milky white sodium rich plagioclase feldspar. The dark flecks are iron rich mica called biotite - the grey glassy grains are quartz.

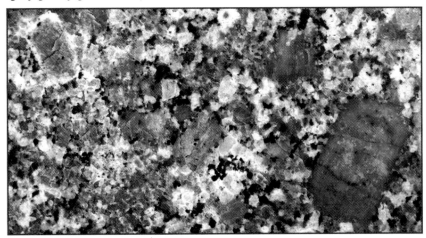

SPANISH PARADE

After walking across the **Wolfe Tone Bridge** constructed of limestone and amphibolite blocks, one comes face to face with **The Spanish Parade (loc.15-figure 3.10)** , and the adjoining streets which preserves much of Galway's medieval character. The piazza area uses Castle Stone in a mosaic pattern. There is imaginative use here of Kilkenny limestone for borders, seating, mooring posts and tree surrounds. The **Spanish Arch (figure 3.10)** was built in 1584.

Fig. 3.10
Spanish parade (loc.15) with the 16th century Spanish Arch in view mainly constructed of limestone. Castle stone paving is matched with Kilkenny limestone flags for the hard landscaping.

The 1651 city map shows a rectangular fort, Ceann na Bhalla, surmounting four arches. However all that remains today is the "Blind Arch", more usually known as the Spanish Arch. The arch itself is constructed of limestone, but also contains amphibolite. The remains of the old city wall that still stand in this area contain rounded blocks of granite and limestone. Behind the Arch, **Nimmo's Restaurant**, named after the Scottish engineer who built most of Galway's 19th century piers, is constructed of similar stone. The **City Museum**, next door, has two limestone pillars on each side of its main door, and a limestone archway over a second, Georgian–style doorway.

Opposite the Spanish Arch stands the remains of **Blake's Castle (loc. 16)**,

29

probably built in the early 16th century, which passed through the hands of the families of O'Halloran, Blake and Morgan of Monksfield. It was at different times both a jailhouse and a corn store. Today only the south wall remains intact, as well as a fraction of the east and west walls. Constructed of local limestone, two examples of cusped trefoil-type windows can be seen in the upper section of the east wall. It has recently been restored and incorporated into **Jury's Inn** which uses limestone cladding on its exterior. **Maggie's Café (loc. 17)**, remodelled in the 19th century, preserves portions of a 17th century dwelling. It serves as a good example of the kind of stonework that is all too often concealed beneath plasterwork and pebbledash.

QUAY STREET and HIGH STREET

Quay St. and High St. also have surviving remains of the medieval city. To complement this and as part of the refurbishment of the inner city, these streets have recently been pedestrianised **(loc.18)**. Flagstones of light grey granite and limestone both from China pave the walkways. Many of the 19th century buildings, have recycled medieval stonework in their reconstruction. In some instances the relatively modern plasterwork has been removed so as to reveal the limestone stonework underneath e.g. at **Gemelles restaurant (loc.19)**. **Seaghan Ui Neachtain's public house (loc. 20)**, and the restaurant next door, originally constituted the town house of "Humanity Dick" Martin. A fine example of a late medieval limestone window can be seen on an upper storey of the restaurant, while the pub displays a 17th century limestone window on its Quay Street facade, as well as an early 17th century door case with an elliptical chamfered arch and a drip label all in local limestone. Across the road, **Wooden Heart (loc. 21)**, a late medieval building dating from 1580 was restored in 1980, and retains a fine late medieval limestone window.

In High St., a late medieval limestone arch with a 15th/16th century drip label fronts **Arch Shoe Repairs (loc. 22)**. **Kenny's Bookshop (loc. 23)** is a 17th century house, whose interior contains three 17th century fireplaces, among other medieval features. The house is better viewed from the Middle St. facade, where the original limestone can be seen, including one of several "1816" stones to be found in the city. The origin of these stones is uncertain, but they are believed to have a religious significance. On the High St. facade, a 17th century window has been converted into a door. **Tom Nally's Barbers (loc. 24)** contains a late medieval limestone doorway. Across the road, in Mainguard St., the **Bank of Ireland (loc. 25)** displays an unusual finish which uses calcite fragments set in cement.

SHOP STREET and WILLIAMSGATE STREET

St. Nicholas' Collegiate Church (loc. 26- figure 3.11) was built in 1320. It is one of the best preserved medieval churches in Ireland and is the oldest surviving building in the city. Constructed of local limestone, it was enlarged during the 15th and 16th centuries. For those interested in more information regarding this majestic building there is a book – *The Story of St. Nicholas' Collegiate Church, Galway*, by Rev. J. Fleetwood (1912) and recently revised by Jim Higgins, Rev., Canon Leslie D. A. Forrest and Derek Biddulph (1989). The obelisk in front of the Church is made from Galway granite and limestone. The obelisk was erected in 1887 and commemorates the tragic death of three young men - John Shelton Thompson, Francis John Langley Kinkead and Thomas

Leopold Roberts. They were drowned on the 17th August 1887 while sailing, one stormy day, on Lough Corrib, on their way to Oughterard. The limestone carving on the front of the obelisk is the Claddagh ring emblem - joined hands supporting a crowned heart - a symbol of love, friendship and loyalty (see the back cover photograph). The right side has the skull and crossbones with the words "Memento mori" - on the left side is an Irish harp and on the back are the arms of Galway.

Fig. 3.11
St. Nicholas' Church (loc. 26) built from local lime-stone in 1320 and subsequently enlarged in the 15th and 16th centuries.

Taaffes (19/20 Shop Street) and **Eason's (loc. 27 - 33** Shop Street) are both good examples of the use of dressed limestone blocks from the Menlough quarries. **Sasha's Boutique (loc. 28- figure 3.12)** at 34 Shop Street, is clad with panels of grey Leinster granite, quarried at Ballybrew, Co. Wicklow, note how crystals of the mineral muscovite reflect the sunlight which is a characteristic of this rock type. At 36 Shop Street **McDonald's (loc. 28-figure 3.13)** is panelled with travertine, which is used by the restaurant chain to decorate its restaurants all over the world. It is quarried near Rome. Travertine is typically banded and displays concentric structures and may contain organic debris. The stone is porous but when used in the exteriors of buildings the pores are injected with a cement, producing filled or stopped travertine. Emperor Augustus practically rebuilt Rome with a variety of the rock known as Lapis Tibertinus. The Romans also used it on the floors of their bath houses, because of its porous non-slip properties.

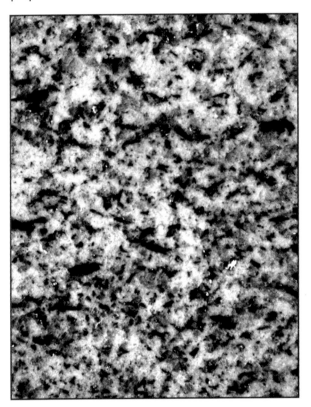

Fig. 3.12
A polished Leinster granite panel from the front of Sasha's boutique. This looks very different to the Galway granite (fig. 3.9). The milky white grains of plagioclase are clearly visible as too are the grey glassy crystals of quartz. The dark rectangular shaped crystals (~1cm long) are the micaceous mineral called muscovite which reflects sunlight producing patches of silvery metallic reflectance.

At 38/39 Shop Street **McCambridge's (loc. 28-figure 3.14)** polished fascia is of _larvikite_ panels and is one of several buildings in the area to use this interest-

Fig. 3.13
One of the pol-
ished   Italian
travertine panels
that clad the front
of   McDonald's.
The   layering   is
characteristic of
this rock type.

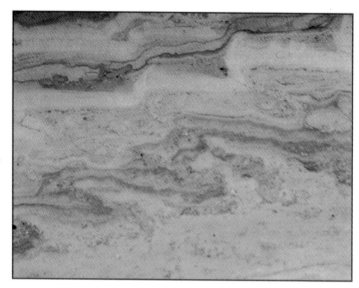

Fig.3.14
Norwegian larvikite panel from
McCambridges shopfront. The
iridescence or schiller effect is
displayed by a number of the
plagioclase feldspars (~2 cm
long) in this view.

ing building stone also used in the Mutton Island project. It is an igneous rock which is quarried at Larvik in southern Norway. It is described as a brilliant blue or green rock whose constituent feldspar crystals catch the weakest sunlight and shimmer, producing a colourful iridescent effect called schillerisation. This schiller effect has led to the immense popularity of this stone in cities throughout the world. Both green and blue varieties, otherwise known in the stone trade as Emerald Pearl and Blue Pearl (or Viking Blue), are used in the city. The variety used here is Emerald Pearl. Another popular construction use for this stone is as an armourstone which means it is used in the construction of harbours and the protection of vulnerable sections of coastline. The Mutton Island sewage project has used larvikite as an armourstone for protection from Atlantic storms.

Across the street a late medieval limestone doorway, dated 1616 and bearing three family coats of arms stands between **River Island** (14 Shop Street) and the **Oriental Restaurant (loc. 29)**. On the first floor of River Island is a 16th century coat of arms, with a dragon. **Esat Digifone (loc. 30)** on the corner offers another fine example of Emerald Pearl polished panels.

Lynch's Castle (loc. 31-figure 3.15) is the only complete secular medieval

Fig. 3.15
The 15th or early 16th century Lynch's Castle constructed from local limestone, at 40 Shop Street.

building in Galway. It was constructed of local Angliham or Menlough limestone in the late 15th to early 16th century. On the Shop St. front there is a rectangular panel showing the coat of arms of King Henry VIII, and a stone roundel containing the coat of arms of the Lynch family. On the Abbeygate St. facade are the coat of arms of the Earl of Kildare. In the foyer of the building, which is now occupied by Allied Irish Banks, there is a 17th century fireplace while panels of Connemara marble adorn sections of the interior space. An interesting feature of the exterior is the sixteen carved limestone gargoyles (water spouts) that can be seen under the parapets.

Fig. 3.16
The Galway Camera Shop (inset - loc. 34) panelled with Verde Ubatuba (or Green Pearl) - a coarse grained feldspar rich igneous rock from Brazil.

Powell's (loc. 32) retains a late 16th century limestone window, as well as two other 16th century drip labels. **Raymond O'Brien's (loc. 33)** shopfront is clad with shimmering Emerald Pearl panels. **Galway Camera Shop (loc. 34 - figure 3.16)** has a plaque of Emerald Pearl but the building is clad with a Brazilian igneous rock called a *syenite*, with the exotic trade name Verde Ubatuba sometimes referred to as Green Pearl. Dark grey panels of South African *norite* (see Fallers below) are used at the base of the shopfront. At 17 Williamsgate Street, **Sweets at Twelve (loc. 34- figure 3.17)** is clad with a fossiliferous limestone known as "Merlin Black", from the now disused quarry at Merlin Park. Large fos-

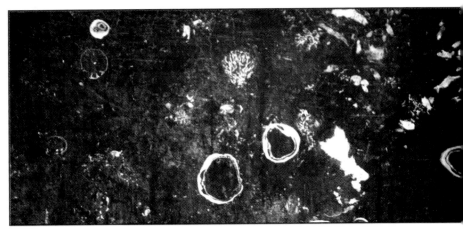

Fig. 3.17 Opposite page
One of three buildings that use panels of the Merlin Black Limestone which was quarried at Merlin. Here at Sweets at Twelve (loc. 34) corals and brachiopod fossils composed of white calcite contrast with the foil of black muddy limestone. Similar panels are used at the Imperial Hotel (loc. 36) and at Curran's Hotel (loc. 50-fig.3.23)

Fig 3.18
Close-up view of a Burlington slate panel from Hanley and Co.'s shopfront at Williamsgate Street (inset—loc. 35). It is quarried near Grizebeck in Cumbria. Variations in grainsize are visible and reflect different sedimentary layers or beds

sil brachiopod and corals are clearly visible - the white calcite of the fossils contrasts well with the black colour of the host limestone. Across the street at 10A/B Williamsgate Street, **Faller's Jewellers (loc. 35)** is clad with norite imported from Bushveld in South Africa and commonly referred to as Black Granite. **Hanley and Co. (loc. 35- figure 3.18)** use polished panels of slate from the English Lake District. Although quarried by Burlington Slate Ltd. for over 150 years it is a recent addition to the imported stone inventory of Galway. This particular variety is known as Broughton Moor and some of the original sedimentary layering can still be seen.

The front of the **Ulster Bank (loc. 36- figure 3.19)** at 33/34 Eyre Square has been recently reclad using polished panels of the distinctive and spectacular Rapakivi granite known as Baltic Brown from Southern Finland. It displays a crystal growth texture termed Rapakivi texture which accounts for its geological name. The type locality is Kengis in southern. Finland. The texture displays rounded reddish to pink feldspar crystals (2-3cm across) mantled by a second

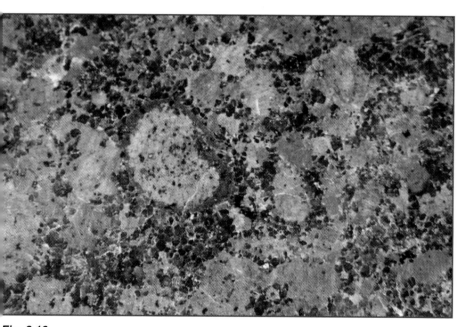

Fig. 3.19.
This spectacular granite known in the stone trade as Baltic Brown is used here to clad the front of the Ulster Bank (loc. 36). Pink orthoclase feldspars (~3 cm across) displaying a rim composed of another variety of feldspar (i.e. plagioclase) constitute the characteristic rapakivi texture of this distinctive granite quarried at Rapakivi, Finland.

growth of a different type of feldspar. The **Imperial Hotel (loc. 36)** is panelled with Merlin Black limestone and bears the city's coat of arms. Both Emerald and Green Pearl panels are used on the front of 3 Williamsgate Street, **Eire Communications (loc. 37-figure 3.20)**. The upper storey of 1 Williamsgate Street, **Abrakebabra (loc. 37)** is clad with panels of Connemara marble and of Norwegian *schist*.

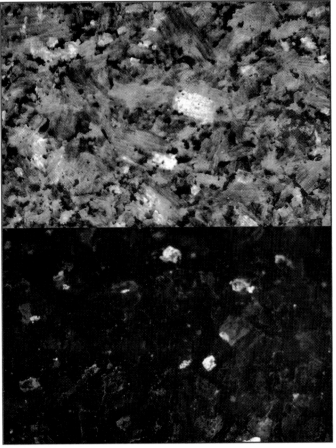

Fig. 3.20
The front of Eire Communications (loc. 37) utilises polished panels of two Norwegian larvikites - the green larvikite called Emerald Pearl (also used elsewhere in the city) and the blue larvikite called Blue Pearl or Viking Blue.

EYRE SQUARE-PROSPECT HILL

Eyre Square (loc. 38) was Galway's first public park, officially presented to the city in 1710 by Mayor Edward Eyre. The **Browne Doorway** was removed from its original site in Abbeygate St. to Eyre Square in 1905. The limestone structure has an arched door case, surmounted by a window. It contains a "marriage stone" bearing the arms of Martin Browne and Marie Lynch, dated 1627. The statue of **Padhraic O'Conaire** by Albert Power, probably the city's best-known landmark, was unveiled by Eamon De Valera in 1935. Both monuments are constructed of Menlough limestone. The **John F. Kennedy lectern** commemorates the President's visit to Galway in 1963, and is clad with Ballinasloe limestone. The fourth predominant structure in the square is the 1984 **Quincentennial Fountain** and metal sculpture by Eamon Doherty, depicting the sails of a Galway Hooker, presented to the city by the Bank of Ireland.

The **National Irish Bank (loc. 39)** is clad with panels of a red granite from Finland. It is known commercially as "Balmoral Red". Further down the **Eyre Square shopping centre (loc. 40)** offers a diversion. In the course of excavations prior to the construction of the centre, a further section of the old city wall was discovered, including the bases of two medieval towers. The crumbling city wall has been restored, and the two towers reconstructed, although not to their original height. The stonework employed in the reconstruction corresponds to that found in the original remains. **Penrice's Tower** has been rebuilt of limestone, while a mixture of limestone, granite and sandstone has been used in the reconstruction of **Shoemaker's Tower**, and the wall itself. Back on the west side of the Square, next door to the shopping centre, the **Bank of Ireland (loc. 41)**, formerly the National Bank, is an Italianate version of 19th century Irish architecture. Designed by William Calbeck, it was built in 1863 of Menlough limestone. It displays fine Doric porches with interesting architectural features. Ballinasloe limestone panelling adorns a recent extension to the bank.

Across the road, on the southern side of the Square, the **Allied Irish Bank (loc. 42)** building is clad with Ballinasloe limestone, in which brachiopod fragments are clearly visible. An interesting feature of the panels here is the circular sawmarks left behind by the blade as it cut through the blocks of limestone at the quarry. The **Great Southern Hotel (loc. 43)** and the **Railway Station (loc. 44)** were designed by J.S. Mulvaney in 1851 for the Midland and Great Western Railway Company. It is constructed of limestone over a ground floor of rusticated limestone blocks. In the foyer of the hotel is a fireplace made from Connemara marble.

On the east side of the Square limestone cladding adorns the **Irish Nationwide (loc. 45)** building at number 11, while **O'Connell's Pub (loc. 45)** at number 8 is clad with Emerald Pearl. **NTL (loc. 46)** at Odean House, uses Galway granite blocks in contrast to **Church and General, Irish Life** and the **EBS (loc. 46)** all in Hardiman House, which are all clad with Ballinasloe limestone.

Richardson's (loc. 47 -figure 3.21) public house at 1 Eyre Square is clad with

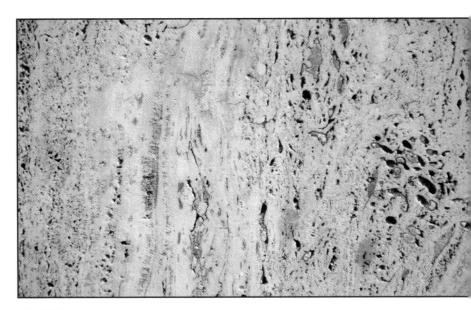

Fig. 3.21
The Italian travertine at Richardson's public house (loc. 47). Compare with the more recently erected panels on McDonald's (loc. 28-fig. 3.13) and note the weathered state of the older panels.

travertine panels which have undergone serious erosion over the years compared with the panels at McDonalds which are of more recent construction. Around the corner at 8 Prospect Hill, the **Trustee Savings Bank (loc. 48)** displays columns of Ballinasloe limestone with decorative carving work. **The Quad Pub (loc. 48- figure 3.22)** at 12/14 Prospect Hill, is clad with polished granite panels of Balmoral Red similar to that displayed on the front of National Irish Bank on the western side of Eyre Square. Across the road **Curran's Hotel (loc. 49-figure 3.23)** is panelled with Connemara marble quarried at Streamstown. Note the way the marble panels are matched using the cutting and polishing process called quartering already referred to in the context of the Cathedral's interior panels. Below the panels of marble the base is clad with local limestone panels. Moving back towards Eyre Square the **Bank of Ireland (loc. 50)** building was opened in 1830, and acted as a principal distribution centre for famine relief in the west. The building was probably constructed in the 1780's as a market house, and served as the County Club before being taken over by the bank. In the 19th century the bank was fronted by 50 perches of open ground, on which fairs and markets were traditionally held - it is built of cut Angliham limestone. Finally, The **Galway Advertiser's (loc. 51)** building displays columns and panels of Ballinasloe limestone.

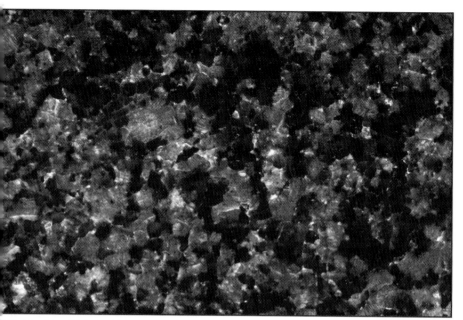

Fig 3.22 (above)
The Quad public house (loc.49) uses polished panels of the distinctive red granite from Finland, called Balmoral Red in the stone trade. National Irish Bank (loc. 39) is also clad with this granite.

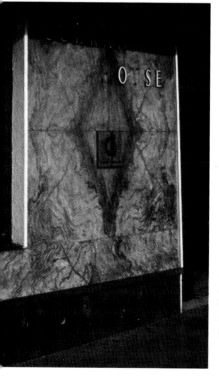

Fig. 3.23 (left)
Exterior view of Curran's Hotel showing the matched panels of Connemara marble with a base of Merlin Black limestone panels.

Glossary

Amphibolite   A metamorphic rock composed mainly of the mineral amphibole.

Basalt   A dark grey, fine-grained, volcanic rock essentially composed of the minerals plagioclase and pyroxene with or without olivine.

Brachiopod   A type of shellfish, often found fossilised in limestones. They were very common during the Carboniferous.

Calcite   A common carbonate mineral (calcium carbonate : $CaCO_3$). Main mineral of limestones and marbles.

Carboniferous   A geological period that began ~362 million years ago and ended about 290 million years ago.

Coral   Fossilised coral that lived in the company of brachiopods in shallow subtropical seas.

Crenulated parapet   Very small indentations like the margins of leaves (crenulated) around a defensive wall or elevation (parapet).

Crinoid   Crinoids are fossilised marine organisms that lived in shallow subtropical seas. They are sometimes called sea lilies. Limestones containing an abundance of this fossil type are called crinoidal limestones.

Dendritic   A form resembling a branching tree.

Dolerite   A fine to medium-grained igneous rock similar to basalt.

Feldspar   An important rock-forming silicate. There are two Feldspar groups i.e. the calcium and sodium bearing Plagioclase feldspars and the Alkali feldspars containing potassium and sodium.

Flagstones   Thinly bedded and easily cleavable dimension stone commonly used for paving.

Fossiliferous	A rock containing an abundance of fossils.
Gabbro	A group of dark-coloured, coarse-grained igneous rocks composed largely of the minerals plagioclase feldspar and pyroxene (a calcium, iron and magnesium bearing silicate mineral).
Gneiss	A metamorphic rock consisting of bands of light and dark minerals- usually the product of very high temperatures and pressures deep within the Earth's crust.
Granite	A coarse grained igneous rock containing quartz feldspar and mica.
Hornblende	An important rock-forming silicate mineral and a member of the amphibole group.
Larvikite	An igneous rock called syenite from Larvik in Norway rich in plagioclase feldspar.
Limestone	A sedimentary rock consisting largely of calcium carbonate i.e. the mineral calcite.
Magma	The molten rock material which forms igneous rocks.
Marble	A metamorphosed limestone.
Mica	An important group of sheet-like silicates characterised by their shiny platy habit and perfect basal cleavage. It includes the minerals biotite (dark in colour containing magnesium and iron) and muscovite (silvery grey in colour containing potassium).
Moss agate	A variety of silica containing dendritic, fern-like patterns and often polished for decorative use.
Mudstones	Fine-grained sedimentary rocks composed chiefly of clay minerals.
Mullioned	Vertical members of stone between the lights of a window.

Muscovite
A common rock-forming mineral that is part of the mica group (see mica above).

Norite
A dark-coloured igneous rock composed essentially of the minerals plagioclase and pyroxene related to gabbro (above).

Olivellites
The name for fossilised sinuous burrowing trails left by an organism -they are characteristic of the Liscannor flagstones.

Quartz
A very important rock forming silicate mineral of simple chemistry i.e. Silicon dioxide ($SiO2$).

Quartzite
A metamorphosed sandstone.

Rhyolite
A volcanic rock essentially composed of the minerals quartz and alkali feldspar.

Sandstone
A sedimentary rock composed of grains of quartz.

Schist
A metamorphosed mudstone exhibiting a sheen on its cleavable surfaces.

Serpentine
A greenish hydrous magnesium silicate of which two forms occur, a fibrous (asbestiform) one known as chrysotile and lamellar one called antigorite.

Serpentinite
A metamorphic rock largely made up of serpentine.

Slate
A fine-grained metamorphic rock that cleaves easily.

Syenite
An coarse grained igneous rock that contains feldspar but little quartz..

Tectonic plates
The surface of the Earth is composed of crustal plates called tectonic plates that are up to 100km thick -they are in constant motion and are responsible for earthquake and volcanic activity.

Tremolite
A white to pale greyish-green mineral of the amphibole group.

References

Administrators of Galway Cathedral. 1980. *Cathedral of Our lady Assumed into Heaven and St. Nicholas Galway.* Shanway Publications Ltd., Glengormley, Northern Ireland.

Coats, J.S. and Wilson, R.J. 1971. The eastern end of the Galway Granite. *Mineralogical Magazine*, 38, 138-151.

Fleetwood, J. 1912. *The story of St. Nicholas' Collegiate Church, Galway.* revisions and additions by Higgins, J., Forrest, L.D.A. and Biddulph, D. 1989).

Garner, W. 1985. *National Heritage Inventory. Galway Architectural Heritage.* Published by An Foras Forbartha, Dublin.

Harper, D.A.T. (ed.) 1996. *An Irish Geological Time Capsule- The James Mitchell Museum University College, Galway.* Published by James Mitchell Museum, NUI, Galway. Printed by Standard Printers Galway.

Kinahan, G.H. 1869. Geological Description of Sheets 105, 104. Memoirs of the Geological Survey of Ireland.

Kinahan, G.H. 1886. Irish Marbles and Limestones. *Scientific Proceedings of the Royal Dublin Society,* 372-444.

Leake, B.E. and Tanner, P.W.G. 1994. *The Geology of the Dalradian and Associated Rocks of Connemara, Western Ireland.* A report to accompany the :63,360 geological map & cross-sections of Connemara. Royal Irish Academy.

O'Heideain, E. (ed.) 1991. *The Dominicans in Galway 1241-1991.* Published by Dominican Priory, Galway.

Press, F. and Siever, R. 1998. *Understanding the Earth.* Published by W.H. Freeman and Co., New York.

Smith, M.R. (ed.). 1999. *Stone: Building Stone, Rock Fill and Armourstone in Construction.* Engineering Geology Special Publ. 16. Geol. Society, London.

Wager, L.R. 1932. The geology of the Roundstone district, Co. Galway. *Proceedings of the Royal Irish Academy,* **41B**, 46-72.

Wilkinson, G. 1845. *Practical Geology and Ancient Architecture of Ireland.* Published by J. Murray, London.

Recommended reading

Branney, M.J. 1983. The ornamental and building stones of Stoke-on-Trent Staffordshire Geological Recording Scheme -Publication No. 1, 51pp.

Mc Call, J., 1999. *Gloucester in Stone*. Published by Thematic Trails (Pete Keane ed.), Kingston Bagpuize, Oxfordshire.

Pavia, S. and Bolton, J. 2001. *Stone monuments decay study 2000*. Publishe(by The Heritage Council. 228pp + CD.

Pavia, S. and Bolton, J. 2001. *Stone, brick and mortar: Historical Use, Deca and Conservation of Building Materials in Ireland*. Published by Wordwell Ltd. Bray. 296pp.

Williams, D.M. and Harper, D.A.T. 1999. The Making of Ireland. Landscapes i Geology. 98pp, Immel Publishing, London.

Wyse Jackson, P. 1993. *The Building Stones of Dublin -A Walking Guide* Published by Town House and Country House, Donnybrook, Dublin. 67pp.

To find out more about geology

Geology Department in NUI Galway
Activity sheets are available on request for National Schools and Secondar' Schools. The James Mitchell Museum is open to visitors in the Quadrangl(Building of the University, displaying fine rock mineral and fossil collections an(explaining local geology.
Contact: martin.feely@nuigalway.ie

Geoscapes
This guide is the first in a planned series of guidebooks to be published b' Geoscapes. Look for others covering different areas and topics. Geoscape also sell an extensive range of books and maps covering the geology and land scape of Ireland. Send for a booklist and look out for Geoscapes selling book at most major geological meetings.

Irish Geological Association
This organisation caters for amateur and professional geologists alike and is very friendly group. Lectures are organised in different centres around the coun try such as Dublin, Galway, Belfast and Cork, mainly during autumn to sprin(

me. Throughout the year, mainly in spring and autumn, weekend field excursions are organised to all areas of Ireland. A regular newsletter is also issued to members. Contact the IGA through the Geological Survey of Ireland or any University Geology Department.

ES2K - Earth Science 2000

This is a mainly Northern Ireland based organisation set up to promote geology in Northern Ireland, partly as a response to serious pressures on the teaching of geology in schools and university. Like the IGA, it is a dynamic organisation and is a great forum for enthusiasts to learn more. An excellent newsletter is issued and both members and the area of activity is not restricted to Northern Ireland.

Galway Naturalists' Field Club

Dr Colin Lawton (Treasurer of the Galway Naturalists' Field Club)
c/o Zoology Department, NUI Galway, Galway

Email: galwaynaturalists@eircom.net
Web: http://homepage.eircom.net/~gnfc

Irish Journal of Earth Sciences

This academic journal is published by the Royal Irish Academy and includes papers on the full spectrum of geology, geomorphology and earth science. Subscription is very reasonable, but it should also be available for consultation in many libraries.
www.ria.ie

Geological Survey of Ireland

This is the national agency for earth science information and provides maps and publications and other data on the full spectrum of geology. It has a library, exhibition area and shop open to the public as well as a full enquiry service. Contact the GSI at Beggars Bush, Haddington Road, Dublin 4. Telephone 01-6707444/6041420 or access the website: www.gsi.ie

Geological Survey of Northern Ireland

This is the national agency for geology in Northern Ireland and covers the full spectrum of services. Contact GSNI at 20 College Gardens, Belfast BT9 6BS. Telephone 028-90666595. Fax 028-90662835 gsni@bgs.ac.uk

Geological Museum, Trinity College Dublin

The Museum is part of the Department of Geology which also maintains a large and well stocked geological library. The museum is normally accessible to the public during working hours or by appointment. Contact the Museum Curator, D Patrick Wyse Jackson or the Department Secretary. The Department also runs occasional lecture courses of general interest during the autumn. Details usual ly available in Dublin evening class listings.

Department of Geology, University College Dublin
The Department also runs occasional lecture courses of general interest during the autumn. Details usually available in Dublin evening class listings.

Department of Geology, University College Cork
The Department also runs occasional lectures of general interest. Like all the geology departments individual staff may be able to help with identification o specimens or study advice. The Cork Geological Association may also be con tacted through the Geology Department.

The Open University
The Open University has an office in Belfast for Ireland and runs a range of dis tance learning geology courses which can be studied independently with tutori al support, and occasional sessions at different centres around Ireland. The geology courses can be taken without necessarily leading to a full degree course.

The Mining Heritage Trust of Ireland
All aspects of mining and quarrying and extraction are the concern of this organ isation, with a focus on fieldmeetings, conservation of key remains and raising awareness of the importance of mining heritage. See www.mhti.com

Acknowledgements

We would like to thank the Heritage Council for assisting with the publication o this book. We acknowledge the advice, support and invaluable information given to us by John Cotter (Top Quarries, Ballinasloe), Ambrose Joyce Snr. and Ambrose Joyce Jnr. (Connemara Marble Industries Ltd., Moycullen) and Martin Walsh (Proprietor, Costelloe Murvey Granite Quarry) during the course of this project. Thanks to Bishop McLoughlin, Fr. May, Rector Towers and Fr. Reynolds O.P. for their assistance during the research for the book. Dr. Pat Morgan's (Dean of Science, NUI, Galway) timely support and encouragement is gratefully acknowledged. Thanks to Christine Hunt for advice and comments on the text.